Oxford
Progressive
English Readers

A MIDSUMMER NIGHT'S DREAM AND OTHER STORIES FROM SHAKESPEARE'S PLAYS

The *Oxford Progressive English Reader*s series provides a wide range of reading for learners of English.

Each book in the series has been written to follow the strict guidelines of a syllabus, wordlist and structure list. The texts are graded according to these guidelines; Grade 1 at a 1,400 word level, Grade 2 at a 2,100 word level, Grade 3 at a 3,100 word level, Grade 4 at a 3,700 word level and Grade 5 at a 5,000 word level.

The latest methods of text analysis, using specially designed software, ensure that readability is carefully controlled at every level. Any new words which are vital to the mood and style of the story are explained within the text, and reoccur throughout for maximum reinforcement. New language items are also clarified by attractive illustrations.

Each book has a short section containing carefully graded exercises and controlled activities, which test both global and specific understanding.

A Midsummer Night's Dream
and Other Stories
from Shakespeare's Plays

Edited by David Foulds

Hong Kong
Oxford University Press
Oxford Singapore Tokyo

Oxford University Press

Oxford   New York   Toronto
Kuala Lumpur   Singapore   Hong Kong   Tokyo
Delhi   Bombay   Calcutta   Madras   Karachi
Nairobi   Dar es Salaam   Cape Town
Melbourne   Auckland   Madrid

and associated companies in
Berlin   Ibadan

Oxford is a trade mark of Oxford University Press

First published 1992
Third impression 1993

© Oxford University Press 1992

Illustrated by Choy Man Yung

Syllabus designer: David Foulds

Text processing and analysis by Luxfield Consultants Ltd.

ISBN 0 19 585261 3

Printed in Hong Kong
Published by Oxford University Press (Hong Kong) Ltd
18/F Warwick House, Tong Chong Street, Quarry Bay, Hong Kong

CONTENTS

A MIDSUMMER NIGHT'S DREAM

Chapter One

Prince Theseus, the ruler of Athens, was going to be married. He was going to marry Hippolyta, Queen of the Amazons.

One day, just a few days before his wedding, a rich *5*
old man named Egeus came to see him. Egeus wanted to talk to Prince Theseus about something that was making him very angry.

Egeus had a daughter called Hermia, and he had chosen a man named Demetrius to be her husband. *10*
However, Hermia said she would not marry Demetrius. She loved another young man, called Lysander.

Egeus was angry with Hermia. He said she must do as he told her, or die. That was what the laws of Athens allowed in those days. *15*

The Prince listened to what Egeus had to say. He told Hermia that she must obey her father, but she said she loved Lysander, and wanted to marry him.

Lysander told the Prince that Demetrius used to love Hermia's best friend, Helena. He said that Helena still *20*
loved Demetrius, and that Demetrius ought to marry her.

Theseus felt sorry for Hermia, but he could not let her break the law. He told her that she must marry Demetrius. If she did not, then she must either die, or *25*
become a nun for the rest of her life. As a nun she would live far from her home and friends. She would spend all her time working, and praying to God.

The Prince was to be married in four days' time. Hermia was allowed those four days in which to give him her answer.

Hermia and Lysander plan to run away

5 Hermia was very unhappy. She went to see Lysander. Together they planned to leave Athens.

Lysander had a rich aunt who lived twenty miles away. There were no laws of Athens there, because it was a different country.

10 'We can go to my aunt's house,' said Lysander, 'and then we can be married. Tomorrow night, leave home very quietly. Then meet me in the wood outside Athens. Meet me at the place where we used to play when we were children.'

15 While they were talking, Helena joined them. She was Hermia's best friend, so they told her what they were going to do.

Helena did not keep their secret. Later, she told Demetrius all about it. She said she would show
20 Demetrius where Hermia and Lysander planned to meet. She loved Demetrius very much. She hoped he would love her if she helped him.

Fairies and elves

The wood, where Hermia and Lysander were going to meet, was the home of elves and fairies. These magic little people looked after the flowers and the trees, and all the animals. They liked to work and play games all night in the open spaces of the wood. 5

If they were happy, everything in the world was all right, but for some months, they had been very unhappy. Their King and Queen, Oberon and Titania, were angry with each other. They often quarrelled, and then the elves and fairies ran and hid because they were afraid. 10

King Oberon and Queen Titania were always quarrelling about a little boy. His mother had died, and the Queen had been looking after him. She had made him her servant-boy. Oberon did not like this. He wanted the boy to be his servant, but Titania would not give the boy to him. 15

On the night when Hermia and Lysander planned to meet in the wood, Titania and Oberon also met there. Once again, they quarrelled. Oberon asked Titania to give him the boy. Titania said she would not. Oberon became very angry. 20

25

He thought of a way to make Titania do what he wanted. When Titania and her fairies had gone away to another part of the wood, Oberon called to one of his elves. The name of this elf was Puck.

Puck's work

Puck loved to be bad. He liked to play tricks on the village people. When the women did their cooking, he made everything go wrong. When the children were playing, he jumped at them so they shouted with fright. When people came into the wood, he led them about so that they got lost. Once, he pretended to be a chair. A fat old woman saw him. She decided to sit on him. She was very old, and very fat, so she sat down very slowly. As she was sitting down, Puck moved away. Of course, down she fell, on to the floor! Puck thought that was very funny.

'Come here, Puck,' said Oberon. 'I want you to go and get me a special flower. The name of the flower is "Love-in-idleness". It is a magic flower. When Queen Titania is asleep I will put some of the juice of the flower on to her eyes. When she opens her eyes, she will fall in love with the first thing she sees. I hope she will look at something really ugly. Then she will come to me and ask me to take the magic away. Before I do, I will make her give that child to me.'

Puck went to find the flower. He had to go half way round the world, but he could fly very fast. He loved doing work like this.

Oberon sees Helena and Demetrius

While Oberon was waiting for Puck to return, Demetrius came into the wood. He was looking for Hermia. After him came Helena. She was chasing Demetrius.

Demetrius and Helena did not see Oberon, but he watched them and he listened to them talking. He heard Demetrius scold Helena for following him.

'I don't love you, so go away! Just stop following me about all the time!' he said. He was angry with her.   5

'Oh, when you are angry I love you even more,' said Helena. 'When you tell me to go away, you make me want to follow you, dear Demetrius!'

This made Demetrius even more angry. He ran away towards some other part of the wood very quickly. He   10 hoped Helena would not be able to follow him, but she could run fast, too.

Oberon watched them go. He felt very sorry for Helena, and decided to help her. He would use some of   15 the juice from "Love-in-idleness" to make Demetrius fall in love with her.

When Puck returned with the juice, he said to him, 'In this wood there is a beautiful lady from Athens. She is in love with a young man who keeps running away   20 from her. Go and find them. Make them feel tired. When they go to sleep put the juice on the man's eyes, and turn his head so that he is looking towards the lady. When he wakes up she will be the first thing he sees, and then he will fall in love with her.'   25

'How will I know which man you mean?' asked Puck.

'He is wearing Athenian clothes,' said King Oberon. Puck went away to do this new work.

Titania falls asleep

Oberon had kept some of the juice for himself. He went   30 to look for Titania.

After a little while, he found her. She was getting ready to go to sleep. Secretly, he watched her giving

her fairies their orders for the night. She told some to
bring birds' wings to make fairy coats. Others had to go
and kill the bad insects in the flowers. Some were to
frighten away a bird whose noisy cry might stop Titania
5 from sleeping. She asked two or three to stay with her.
They had to sing softly and help her fall asleep.

As soon as she was sleeping, the fairies went away.
Then, very quietly, Oberon came. He put some of the
juice from the flower on her eyes. As he
10 did so he said, softly, 'You will fall in
love with the first thing you
see when you wake
up.' Then he left.

Chapter Two

Hermia and Lysander had met in the wood. They were on their way to Lysander's aunt's house, but they had lost the path. Hermia was tired and so they sat down for a rest. It was not long before they both fell asleep. 5

Puck was running through the wood, looking for the beautiful lady and the man in Athenian clothes. He found Hermia and Lysander lying on the ground, asleep. Hermia was beautiful. She and Lysander both came from Athens, so Lysander was wearing Athenian 10 clothes.

Puck thought that these two people were the people Oberon had told him about. He turned Lysander's head so that he was facing Hermia. Then he quickly put the juice from the flower on Lysander's eyes and went 15 away.

Everything would have been all right if the first person Lysander looked at when he woke up had been Hermia. He loved her already. But during the night, Helena came through the wood. 20

She was tired. She had been running so fast, trying to catch Demetrius. She stopped to rest.

Lysander falls in love with Helena

In the dark she could not see Hermia, but she saw Lysander. She nearly stepped on him. She was surprised. 25 She did not know why Lysander was lying on the ground, there. She thought he might be dead. She was quite frightened, and tried to wake him up. Of course, now the first thing that Lysander saw when he woke up was Helena's face! So Lysander fell in love 30 with Helena.

'You are the most beautiful woman I have ever seen,'
he said to her. 'I love you so much that I would run
through fire for you.'

Helena did not know anything about King Oberon
or the juice of the flower "Love-in-idleness". When
Lysander spoke lovingly to her, she thought he was
5 making fun of her. She thought that he was really in
love with Hermia. She was sad and angry, and ran away
from him. But he followed her. He had forgotten all
about Hermia.

Hermia woke up. She had been dreaming, and her
10 dream had frightened her. She wanted to tell Lysander
about it, but she could not see him anywhere. She was
even more frightened. Perhaps a large wild animal had
killed Lysander and taken him away, she thought. She
went to look for him. She walked on and on through
15 the wood, calling Lysander's name.

So now the four young people were all alone in
different parts of the wood – Demetrius was looking for
Hermia, Helena was looking for Demetrius, Lysander
was looking for Helena, and Hermia was looking for
20 Lysander.

The Athenian actors

In the early hours of the morning, some more people
came into the wood. They were young men from
Athens. One of them had written a play. They were
25 going to act the play at the wedding of Prince Theseus.
They had come to the wood to practise their parts.
Their acting was really very bad, but they were serious
about it. They hoped that the Prince would enjoy their
play.

30 Puck had finished his work. He was returning to King
Oberon. On his way, he saw the young men acting.

He watched them secretly. He thought they were very foolish. In the middle of their acting, he played one of his tricks upon them.

One young man was bigger and more foolish than the others. His name was Bottom. Bottom was pretending to be a man in love. In one part of the play he had to change his clothes. He went behind a tree to put his new clothes on.

Puck did something to Bottom's head. He made his head look like the head of a donkey. It was very ugly.

Bottom did not know about this. He just put on his new clothes. Then he stepped out from behind the tree. The other young men saw him. They shouted with fright. Bottom had not just changed his clothes, he had changed his head, too! He looked horrible! They were very frightened, and they all ran away.

Bottom did not know why they had run away from him. He thought they were playing a trick on him. He thought they were just pretending to be frightened of him.

Bottom was alone in the wood. It was very dark. He was quite frightened, too. He started to sing a song. That would make him feel better, he thought.

Titania falls in love

Titania was asleep nearby and Bottom's singing woke her up. When she opened her eyes, the first thing she saw was Bottom, with his donkey's head.

Titania fell in love with him at once! She asked Bottom to sing for her. She made a circle of flowers and put it on his head. Then she sang him to sleep with lovely songs.

While she was doing all this, Oberon came and scolded her for being so foolish. Titania felt very silly. She gave him the child. They would not quarrel any more about him.

When he got what he wanted, Oberon took away the magic which had made Titania fall in love with Bottom. He told Puck to make Bottom's donkey's head go away and give him back his real head. Then they all left Bottom lying on the ground, asleep.

Bottom woke up. He could remember some strange things, but he never really knew what had happened to him. He went to look for his friends.

Chapter Three

Hermia was still looking for her lost Lysander. On her way through the wood, she met Demetrius. Oberon was close by, and he heard them talking.

Hermia said that she thought Demetrius had done 5 something bad to Lysander. She asked Demetrius to bring Lysander back.

Demetrius did not understand, but he could see that Hermia was still in love with Lysander. He was very angry with Lysander, and went to look for him. He 10 wanted to fight him.

Oberon could see that something had gone wrong. He wanted to set things right between the young people. He sent Puck to find Helena and bring her to where Demetrius was sleeping. He himself dropped 15 the juice on Demetrius's eyes. He hoped that when Demetrius woke up he would see Helena and fall in love with her. Then, he thought, Lysander and Hermia, Helena and Demetrius would all be happy together. But he had forgotten that Lysander was now in love 20 with Helena, not Hermia!

Helena and Hermia quarrel

Helena and Lysander both came to where Demetrius was asleep. Demetrius woke up. The first person he 25 saw was Helena, and he fell in love with her.

Then Demetrius began to speak lovingly to Helena. This surprised the poor lady very much. Before, she had not been loved by either of the men. Now they both said they loved her. She thought that they had joined 30 together to make fun of her.

Hermia came towards them. She had once been loved by both men, but now she was not loved by either! She asked Lysander why he had left her. He only answered her in a very rough voice. Demetrius turned away from her, too.

Helena thought this was all very strange. She thought Lysander and Demetrius were pretending that they did not like Hermia. She began to believe that Hermia knew what was happening, and that she was also in this game. She thought that all three had planned together to make fun of her. She became very angry.

Hermia said Helena had taken Lysander from her, and the two young women began to quarrel.

Lysander and Demetrius went away to fight each other. The winner would marry Helena, they said. That made Hermia and Helena quarrel even more!

Puck sets things right

At last Oberon thought of a way to make things end happily.

First, he told Puck to stop Lysander and Demetrius fighting.

Puck could make his voice sound like the voice of another person. Oberon told him to copy the voices of Demetrius and Lysander. First he must pretend to be Lysander, calling Demetrius. Then he must pretend to be Demetrius shouting to Lysander. It was very dark in the wood, and by copying their voices, he could lead them away from each other. Then they would not be able to start fighting.

'Do this until they are tired,' said Oberon. 'When they fall asleep, drop the juice of this other magic flower into Lysander's eye. This will make him remember his love for Hermia again. Demetrius will still be in love Helena.'

Puck did as he was told. Then he led the four young people about in the wood so that in the end they became tired, and went to sleep. They did not know it, but they all went to sleep quite close to each other.

A happy ending

Hermia was the first to wake up. When she found her lost Lysander asleep near her, she began to ask herself why he had left her so strangely and why he had come back. Did he still love her? Lysander, when he woke, became his old self once more. He loved Hermia as much as ever.

For Helena too, the night ended happily. When she woke up she found that Demetrius really did love her. Hermia and Helena became friends again. However, they could still not be truly happy. Old Egeus had said that his daughter Hermia was to marry Demetrius, or die. What could they do about that cruel law?

They did not have to think about it for long. Prince Theseus and Queen Hippolyta were out riding on their horses early that morning. With them had come Hermia's father, Egeus. As they were riding through the wood, they met the young lovers. Of course Theseus wanted to know what they were doing there at that time. Lysander told him how Hermia and he had planned to run away from Athens and the cruel law.

When Egeus heard this, he at once said that Theseus should punish them for trying to cheat Demetrius. But Demetrius, feeling quite foolish, said that he no longer wanted to marry Hermia. He was now in love with Helena.

When Prince Theseus saw that the four young people were so happy, he made Egeus agree not to ask to have them punished. He also said that they should all be married, with himself and Hippolyta, on his wedding day.

So the strange things that happened on that midsummer night had a happy ending after all.

TWELFTH NIGHT

Chapter One

There once lived, in the land of Greece, a brother and a sister, called Sebastian and Viola. They were twins. They were exactly the same age, and they looked very much alike. When their clothes and hair were alike too, their friends found it difficult to know who was the boy and who was the girl.

They had no parents. Their mother had died when they were very young, and their father had died when they were only thirteen years old. Sebastian and Viola were alone in the world, so they loved each other very much. They were only really happy when they were together.

On the shores of Illyria

When this story begins, Sebastian and his sister were on a ship going to a country called Illyria. There was a bad storm and the ship was broken into pieces by the sea.

Many people could not swim, and were drowned, but Viola was lucky. With the captain and a few men from the ship, she got to the shore in a small boat.

When she had stepped out of the boat, Viola asked the captain if he knew where they were.

'This is Illyria, lady,' said the captain.

Viola was sad because Sebastian was not with her. She hoped that he had been lucky too, and that he was still alive. The captain told her that he had seen Sebastian tie himself to a strong piece of wood before the ship went under the water. He thought that Sebastian had not died.

This was good news, and Viola began to feel happier. She looked around her and asked herself what she ought to do.

A Prince in love

The captain told her that he knew the country well. He had been born there. The ruler of this country was a Prince named Orsino. He was a good man, but he was unhappy. He loved a lady named Olivia, and wanted to marry her, but she did not love him.

'Who is Olivia?' asked Viola. The captain told her that Olivia was the daughter of a rich man who had died a year ago. After his death, Olivia was looked after by her brother. But he, too, had died, and Olivia was so sad that she never left the house or let anyone go to visit her.

Viola felt very sorry for the poor lady. She knew how it felt to lose a much loved brother.

She wanted to go and work for Olivia as her servant, but the captain said that she could not. Since her brother died, Olivia had allowed no one to enter the house, not even Prince Orsino, who loved her.

Viola becomes a servant-boy

'Then,' said Viola, 'if I cannot work for the lady, I shall work for the Prince himself. You, captain, must help me, and I will pay you well. Get me some clothes and I will dress myself as a young man. Then take me to the Prince and tell him I want to be his servant-boy. I will sing to him and work hard for him. But do not tell anyone who I really am.' The captain agreed to Viola's plan and he promised to keep her secret.

Viola gave him some money and he bought her the clothes she wanted. When she was dressed in the clothes, she looked exactly like her brother, Sebastian.

Then the captain took Viola to see the Prince.

Prince Orsino liked the look of the boy (he thought Viola was a boy). He agreed that this 'boy' should be his servant. Viola now called herself Cesario, and no one but the captain knew that she was a girl dressed as a boy.

Viola worked hard and Orsino was very pleased with her. He told her all about his love for Olivia. He told her that the lady refused to see him. She would not keep the presents and letters he sent to her by his messengers.

Viola, as she listened to his story, began to fall in love with the Prince. But she did not show her love for her master.

Viola takes a message

One day, the Prince sent Viola with a love-letter to Olivia. 'Go to the lady,' he said, 'and tell her that I love her. She is not kind to me, but she is the only one that I love. You are still a boy and she may listen to you. If I sent an older man, she would send him away without letting him say anything.'

So, although Viola herself loved the Prince, she went to Olivia's house to try to make the lady marry him. She felt very unhappy as she walked along. When she arrived at the door of Olivia's house, the servant would not let her in.

'The lady is ill,' he said, 'and no one may see her.'

'I know she is ill,' replied Viola, 'that is why I have come. I will not go away until you let me in.'

'But she is asleep,' said the man. 'No one can see her now.'

'I know that, too,' said Viola, 'but I will not go until I have talked to her.'

Olivia meets a good-looking young man

The servant went away and told Olivia about Viola. He said that the young 'man' would not go away until he had talked to her. Olivia asked what he looked like.

5 When she heard that he was young and good-looking she wanted to see him, and told her servant to let him in. She felt sure that the messenger had come from Orsino. She covered her face with piece of thin cloth, her veil, saying that once more she would hear what the

10 Prince had to say.

The servant took Viola into a room where several ladies were sitting. One of the ladies had a veil over her face. Viola did not know which lady was Olivia.

Viola said that she had learnt the words she was to

15 say so carefully that it would be silly to say them to the wrong person. At last, after a lot of talking, she learnt that the lady with the veil was Olivia. But she still refused to

20 give her the message until everyone else had left the room.

'My words are for your ears

23 alone,' she said, 'and I ask you to let me see your face as I speak to you.'

Olivia is very beautiful

Now Olivia liked the look of the young man, and the way he spoke. She was far more interested in the messenger himself than in any message from the Prince. So she agreed to let him see her face.   5

When the other ladies had left the room, she took off her veil. As she did so she said, 'I will pull the curtain, and show you the picture. Do you think it is well painted?'

'Very well,' replied the servant-boy, 'you are very   10
beautiful.'

Then Viola told Olivia about Prince Orsino's love; how he thought about her night and day; and how sad he was because she did not love him.

'I shall never love your master,' said Olivia. 'Go back   15
and tell him so. I want no more messages from him. But you may come again to tell me what he does when he hears my message.'

Olivia was quickly falling in love with Viola. She believed that Viola was a young man. She hated to   20
think she might never see him again. She wanted to give him some money, but Viola refused to take it. Viola asked her once again to think kindly of the Prince, then she went away.

The gold ring   25

When the 'young man' had gone, Olivia was surprised to find how quickly she had fallen in love with him. She

tried to think of a way in which she could show the young man, whose name she thought was Cesario, that   30
she loved him. She wanted to make him come back to her. After thinking for a minute or two, she took the gold ring off her

finger and gave it to her servant. The name of this servant was Malvolio.

'Run after the Prince's messenger,' she said to him, 'and give him this ring which he left behind. Tell him I do not want it, and I do not want any other presents from his master. Tell him also that, if he comes again tomorrow, I will explain why I am doing this.'

Malvolio did as he was asked. At first Viola did not understand. She knew that the Prince had not given her a ring to give to Olivia. Then she guessed that Olivia was falling in love with her and wanted to see her again. This was, of course, just what Olivia had hoped.

'Poor lady,' thought Viola, 'it's no use her falling in love with me. Even though I am dressed as a man, I am a woman. I love the Prince. The Prince loves Olivia. Olivia loves me. This problem is too difficult for me to work out. I only hope that, in time, everything will end happily.'

Chapter Two

When Viola returned to the Prince, she told him that her visit had done no good. The lady had said she could never love him. But the Prince would not believe that Olivia meant what she had said. Viola tried to tell him that it was useless to keep on hoping. 5

'If a lady loved you,' she said, 'and you did not love her, you would tell her so. And she would have to take "No" for an answer.'

'That may be so,' answered the Prince, 'but women can't love in the same way as men. No lady could love 10 a man as much as I love Olivia!'

'I know one who can,' replied Viola. Then she told him how her father's daughter loved a man, but she could never speak to the man about it, and he never knew. 15

Orsino did not know that she was speaking of herself, and of her love for him. He thought she had a sister, and she was telling him about her.

Olivia is in love with Cesario

Orsino told Viola to go again to Olivia and to say that 20 he, Orsino, asked her to marry him. He gave her a piece of jewellery to take as a present for the lady. Viola left once more for Olivia's house.

This time the servant let her in at once, and she was shown into Olivia's room. She began again to ask Olivia 25 to be kind to Orsino. Olivia would not listen.

'But if you have anything to say about yourself,' Olivia said, 'then I will listen gladly.' Of course, Olivia thought Viola was the young man, Cesario.

Viola did not seem to understand her, so Olivia told 30 her that she was in love with her. Viola did not know what to do or say. She told Olivia that she would never fall in love with any woman, and she left the house.

Sebastian, Viola's brother, is alive

All this time, Viola had never given up hope of seeing her lost brother again. That day, while she was talking to Olivia, a young man came into the town. This was Sebastian, Viola's twin brother.

Sebastian had not died in the storm at sea. After tying himself to a piece of wood, he had been picked up by a ship. He was very tired and very weak, but he was still alive.

The captain of the ship had been kind to him, and they were soon good friends. Three months later they reached Illyria. They reached land near the place where Viola had first stepped on to the shore.

Sebastian wanted to see the town and visit the Prince's palace. The captain, Antonio, thought it might not be safe for Sebastian to go alone, but he did not want to go with him.

Not long before this there had been a great fight at sea between Antonio's ship and one of the Prince's ships. Antonio had hurt the Prince's nephew, and the Prince had given orders for Antonio to be made a prisoner. If he went into the town, someone might know who he was. So he went a little way with Sebastian and then told him to go on alone. He gave Sebastian his purse because he might need some money in the town, and he told him to keep out of danger.

Sir Toby, Sir Andrew, and Malvolio

At this time, also, some strange things were happening in Olivia's house.

Olivia had an uncle called Sir Toby Belch. He was a very fat, noisy old man. He often drank wine, and he usually drank too much of it. That made him sing noisy songs. He often behaved very badly.

For a long time Sir Toby had been trying to make his friend, Sir Andrew Aguecheek, talk to Olivia. He thought Sir Andrew would be a good husband for Olivia.

This made Olivia angry. She did not like Sir Andrew. He pretended to be a strong, brave man, but really he was a weak man. He was also a coward.

One day Olivia's servant, Malvolio, scolded Sir Toby for drinking too much, and for singing very noisy songs. This made Sir Toby angry with Malvolio.

Sir Toby plays a trick on Malvolio

Malvolio was a proud man. He thought that he was quite a special person. He was a good servant to Olivia, but everyone else in the house hated him. He thought he was much better than them.

Olivia's girl-servant, Maria, helped Sir Toby to play a trick on Malvolio. They wanted to make him look stupid.

Maria wrote a letter, copying Olivia's writing, and signing Olivia's name. The letter seemed to say that Olivia was in love with her servant, Malvolio, and that she was writing secretly to him. Malvolio found the letter. He believed it. He thought that Olivia was in love with him.

The letter said that if Malvolio loved Olivia, he must let her know. He must do this by wearing some special clothes which must all be of different, bright colours.

Of course, the next time Malvolio went to see Olivia he was wearing brightly coloured clothes. He looked very foolish. Olivia did not know what was happening, and she became quite angry with him.

Sir Toby Belch was pleased with this joke and he wanted to play another one. This time he decided to play a trick on Sir Andrew Aguecheek and Viola.

Sir Toby starts a fight

Like everyone else, Sir Toby and Sir Andrew thought Viola was a young man called Cesario. Sir Andrew had seen Viola when she visited Olivia. He was very jealous because Olivia seemed to like Cesario very much.

Sir Toby told Sir Andrew that he ought to have knocked Cesario (Viola) down. He said that Sir Andrew must quarrel with Cesario and show Olivia that he, Sir Andrew, was a brave man. So when Sir Andrew saw Cesario next, he started a quarrel. He said that Cesario must fight with him.

Viola was frightened. Sir Toby came and talked to her. He told her that Sir Andrew Aguecheek was good at fighting. Viola did not want to fight, but Sir Toby said she must. He told her that if she did not fight then Sir Andrew would become angry, and kill her!

He told his friend, Sir Andrew, that Viola was strong and brave and good at fighting. He frightened Sir Andrew almost as much as he had frightened the poor girl. Of course, Sir Andrew could not say he did not want to fight. He had to show Olivia how brave he was.

The two agreed to fight. They were both bad at fighting, and they were both frightened. They both believed what Sir Toby told them, though they were afraid of each other. Sir Toby thought it was very funny.

Chapter Three

Sir Andrew Aguecheek and Viola met in the garden of Olivia's house to have their fight. The fight was just beginning, when a stranger arrived.

5   This was Antonio, the captain of the ship that had brought Sebastian to Illyria. He had come to town to look for Sebastian. Now because Viola and Sebastian were twins, and because Viola was dressed in men's clothes, Antonio thought Viola was Sebastian.

10   Antonio was surprised to see his young friend fighting so badly. He pulled out his sword and said that he would fight for him.

Viola was also very surprised. She did not know who Antonio was, but she was pleased that someone had come to help her.

Sir Andrew was far from pleased. This stranger looked as if he really knew how to fight!

Antonio is taken prisoner

Antonio should not have come to town. He had hurt the Prince's nephew in a sea-fight. Almost at once he was seen by some of the Prince's officers, who were passing by Olivia's house. They stopped the fight, and made him their prisoner.

Before they took him away, Antonio turned to Viola (he still thought she was Sebastian) and said, 'I must obey these men. See what has happened because I came into the town to look for you. Please give me back my purse, I shall need it.'

Viola did not know what he was talking about. Here was a man, whom she had never seen before, asking for a purse which she had not got. She said she would give the captain half the money she had with her. It was not much, but she thought it would pay for the help he had given her.

Antonio was sad and angry at the same time. His young friend refused to give him back his purse, and was pretending not to know him!

He told the officers that he had pulled this young man from the sea, where he would have died. He had looked after him and he had been a good friend to him. The officers were not interested. They wanted him to go with them at once. So Antonio was led away. As he went he was still shouting at Viola for behaving so badly towards him, and calling her Sebastian.

Viola guessed that the captain thought she was her brother. She knew that meant her brother must be alive, and in town somewhere.

She would have liked to talk to Antonio, but he had gone. She left the place quickly. She was afraid that if she stayed she might have to start fighting Sir Andrew again.

Sebastian fights Sir Andrew

Soon after this, Sebastian, who was walking round the town, came to Olivia's garden. Sir Andrew saw him and thought he was Cesario.

Sir Andrew knew, now, that Cesario was not a good fighter, so he was feeling brave. He ran up to Sebastian and hit him on the head.

Sebastian was not a coward. He was a good fighter. He hit Sir Andrew and then pulled out his sword, telling Sir Andrew to do the same. Sir Andrew was very surprised.

They had not been fighting for long when Olivia came out of her house. She thought that her dear Cesario was in danger. She called out for them to stop. She ordered Sir Andrew to go away, and took Sebastian into her house.

Olivia meets Sebastian

Sebastian was surprised at the kindness shown to him by a lady he had never seen before. He was even more surprised at the loving words she used when she spoke to him. He asked himself if he was asleep or dreaming. If he was dreaming, he liked the dream and hoped it would continue! He thought the lady might be mad, although she did not seem to be. But he could not explain this love which she showed to him.

After a while, Olivia asked Sebastian to marry her. Sebastian was surprised, but he agreed, for he liked her very much. Olivia promised him that the marriage would stay a secret for as long as he wished.

They went to a little church, and were married. Then Sebastian left his new wife. He wanted to find Antonio. He wanted to talk to Antonio about the 5 strange things that had happened to him.

Orsino goes to see Olivia

Viola returned to her master, Prince Orsino. She told 10 him that Olivia did not want to hear his name ever again. Orsino decided it was time that he went to see Olivia himself. So, taking Viola and some servants with him, he started out for Olivia's house.

When they arrived at the door, they met one of 15 Olivia's servants. Orsino promised him some money if he could make Olivia come out of her house. The man hurried away, and the Prince, his servants and Viola waited outside.

As they stood there, the officers of the law, who 20 had caught Antonio, came along the street with their prisoner. They were looking for the Prince. When they

saw Orsino they led Antonio up to him and told him
that this was the man who had hurt his nephew. They
had found him fighting in the street and had caught
him.

5   When Viola heard what they said, she told her
master how Antonio had helped her, although he was
a stranger to her.

The Prince thinks that Antonio is mad

Now Antonio still thought that Viola was his friend,
10   Sebastian. When he heard her words, he explained
angrily to the Prince how he had dragged this young
man, nearly drowned, from the sea. He told the Prince
what had happened since that morning when they
landed on the shore. He said he had come to town
15   looking for the young man. He was afraid that Sebastian
might get into trouble, and he had come to help him,
even though he knew he might be caught himself.
He said that he had been very kind to Sebastian. He
thought it was bad of Sebastian to refuse to give back
20   his purse and to pretend not to know who he was.

      'You must be mad,' said the Prince. 'For the last three
months this young man has been with me, working in
my palace. But here comes Olivia. Officers, take this
mad person away, I will speak to him later.'

25   Then, turning to Olivia, he said how cruel she had
been to him. But Olivia would not listen. Instead, she
spoke lovingly to Cesario and smiled sweetly at him.

Viola is in trouble

Orsino thought he understood what had happened.
30   The servant-boy whom he had sent so often to Olivia
had made her fall in love with him.

He spoke angrily to Cesario and turned to go. He ordered Cesario to follow him. Viola was only too happy to obey. She did not like Olivia to speak so lovingly to her in front of the Prince.

So, though Olivia asked her several times to stay, she followed her master. As she went, she said to Olivia that she loved her master more than her own life, and more than she would ever love a wife.

Then Olivia forgot her promise to keep the marriage a secret. She cried out, 'Cesario, my husband, stay!'

'Husband?' repeated the Prince in great surprise.

'Yes, my husband,' replied Olivia. 'He will tell you so.'

'No, my lord, I am not her husband,' said Viola.

Olivia sent for the priest who had married her to Sebastian. The priest said it was true that he had married these two, only two hours ago. Though Viola said again and again that it was not true, that she was not married to Olivia, the Prince did not believe her. He told her he never wanted to see her again.

Sebastian and Viola are together again

No one could understand what had happened. Olivia was angry and surprised when Viola said that they were not married. Viola did not know why the priest should say that she had been to a wedding when she knew she had not been there.

Then Sebastian arrived. He first spoke friendly words of greeting to Olivia, calling her his wife. Next he turned eagerly to Antonio, and told him how pleased he was to see him.

Everyone looked surprised when they saw Viola and Sebastian, standing in front of them. They both looked so much alike, and when they spoke they sounded almost the same. No one could tell which was Cesario, which was Sebastian. But the surprise of the brother and sister was greatest of all.

'I do not have a brother,' said Sebastian. 'But if you were a woman, I would think that you were my sister, Viola, whom I thought was drowned.'

Viola marries the Prince

Viola was now able to tell everyone that she was not really a man, but was Sebastian's sister. She told them how she had bought the clothes she was wearing so that she could go and work for the Prince.

Now that everything was explained, Sebastian turned to Olivia and laughed at her for falling in love with a woman, and then marrying a man she did not know. But Olivia seemed happy with the way things had ended.   5

Orsino, seeing that Olivia was really married to another man, remembered how often his servant Cesario had said he would never love a woman as much as he loved his master. He asked Viola to marry him and made her say again that she loved him. Then   10 he took her away, promising that as soon as she was dressed again in women's clothes, she would no longer be his servant-boy, but his wife.

3

ROMEO AND JULIET

Chapter One

Many years ago, in the city of Verona, in Italy, there lived two very rich families. One was named Montague, the other Capulet.

5   These two families had been quarrelling with each other for a long time. The quarrel was so bad that if members of the Capulet family met members of the Montague family in the street they fought each other. They never went into each other's houses.

10   When this story begins, Romeo, the son of Montague, thought he was in love with a beautiful lady called Rosaline. She, however, cared nothing for him. He was very unhappy. He followed her everywhere, trying to make her love him.

15   **Lord Capulet's party**

One day, old Lord Capulet decided to give a party. He asked many beautiful young ladies, one of which was Rosaline, and many good-looking young men. But he did not ask anyone from the Montague family.

20   That morning, Romeo and his cousin, Benvolio, were out walking in the streets of Verona. They met Capulet's servant. He was carrying letters which asked people to come to his master's party.

    The servant stopped Romeo and Benvolio and spoke 25 to them. He did not know who Romeo was. Also, he could not read, so he asked Romeo to read the names on the letters for him.

When Romeo did this, he saw that Rosaline was going to the party. He decided that he would go, too. Benvolio agreed to go with him, and they took Mercutio, a close relative of the Prince of Verona, as well. So that no one would know who they were, they decided to cover their faces with masks.

When the three friends, wearing their masks, arrived at the party, they were greeted by old Lord Capulet. He did not know that behind the masks were members of his enemy's family. He told them to enjoy themselves. So they went in. They ate some food, drank some wine, and danced with the ladies.

Romeo sees Juliet

Then a strange thing happened to Romeo. Until that time the only lady he had liked was Rosaline. Suddenly, among the people dancing, he saw a young lady even more beautiful than Rosaline. He knew that he must meet her and speak to her.

Before he could do anything, however, one of Capulet's nephews, called Tybalt, had seen Romeo. Romeo was wearing a mask, but Tybalt knew who he was.

Tybalt was very angry with Romeo for coming to the party. No one ever asked Montagues to come to a Capulet party. He wanted to fight Romeo and kill him.

But his uncle, the old Lord Capulet, told him not
to be so angry. Lord Capulet would not let
anyone hurt Romeo while he was in his house.
Romeo did not know that Tybalt had seen

5   who he was. As soon as he could, he went
up to the beautiful young lady, and spoke
to her. He told her that he had fallen in
love with her, and she spoke very kindly
to him. But as they were talking, the

10   young lady's nurse came to
her. She told her that
her mother wanted
to see her, and so
the young lady
went away.

15   **A Montague loves a Capulet**

Romeo did not know who the young
lady was. He asked the nurse, and
learned that he had been talking
to the daughter of Lord Capulet

20   himself! He was sorry to find that she
was the daughter of his father's enemy,

but he knew he would happily put his life in danger to win her love.

Juliet, too, was not happy when her nurse told her the name of the young man to whom she had been speaking. She was now in love with the son of her father's enemy. 5

Everyone left Lord Capulet's house at midnight, but Romeo did not go home with his friends. He went back to the Capulets' house. He jumped over the wall of the fruit-garden, which went all the way round the house. 10 He stood in the garden for some time, thinking of his new love. Then Juliet appeared at the open window above him.

At first she did not see her lover, but she spoke his name sadly several times. She cried because he 15 belonged to the hated family of Montague.

Romeo listened, and knew from her words that she was in love with him. He called softly to her, and they talked for a long time about the love they felt for each other. They decided to get married. 20

At last, Juliet's nurse called to her. It was time she went to sleep. Juliet promised Romeo that she would send a messenger to him next day. Romeo must tell the messenger where they should meet for their wedding. And so they said good-night and Romeo left the garden. 25

Romeo and Juliet are married

Romeo did not go back to his own house. He went to talk to his good friend, Friar Lawrence, who was a priest. He wanted to ask Friar Lawrence's advice.

The priest was up early that morning. He was 30 working in his garden when Romeo came to see him. From the look on Romeo's face, and the early hour of the visit, the priest guessed that something was wrong.

When Romeo told him how he had spent the night, and of his love for Juliet, the priest was not pleased. But he could see how serious Romeo was. Then he thought that a marriage between a Capulet and a Montague might help the two families to become friends.

So he agreed to do as Romeo asked. He promised to be the priest at Romeo and Juliet's wedding.

They arranged that the marriage would take place that afternoon. When Juliet's messenger, her nurse, arrived, Romeo said that Juliet must meet him at Friar Lawrence's house. Of course, the marriage would be a secret. Romeo's family would know nothing about it, and neither would Juliet's family

Later that day, after the wedding, Juliet returned to her home. She waited for Romeo to come and see her. He had told her that he would come secretly to the garden around her house, and would take her away with him. Something happened, however, which stopped them from meeting again that day.

Tybalt kills Mercutio

At about the same time that Romeo and Juliet were being married, Benvolio and Mercutio were walking in the streets of Verona. Suddenly, they saw a group of Capulets coming towards them. Leading the group was Tybalt. He was the man who had seen Romeo at the Capulets' party.

Mercutio did not belong to either of the enemy families, but he was a friend of Romeo. Tybalt enjoyed quarrelling and fighting. He came up to Mercutio and said that if he was a friend of a Montague, that was the same as being a Montague! Then there was a quarrel. Tybalt was just about to start fighting with Mercutio, when Romeo himself came that way.

Tybalt then turned to Romeo and called him a wicked man. Romeo, of course, did not want to fight with Tybalt. He was a cousin of his dear Juliet, his wife. So he spoke to him in a friendly way. Mercutio was angry with Romeo for speaking to Tybalt like this. He took 5 out his sword to fight Tybalt himself.

The two began fighting. Benvolio and Romeo did their best to stop them, but Tybalt's sword hit Mercutio, and hurt him badly. Mercutio fell to the ground. He was dying. Then, seeing what he had done, Tybalt and 10 his friends ran away.

Romeo kills his wife's cousin

Romeo could see that Mercutio had not got long to live. Benvolio helped the dying man into a house near by, and they called for a doctor, but it was too late. 15

While this was happening, Tybalt returned to try and find Romeo. Romeo was very unhappy when he saw that Mercutio was dead. He fought with Tybalt and killed him.

Benvolio came back and found Romeo standing by 20 the dead body of Tybalt. He told Romeo to go quickly, before any of the people who were watching thought of making him a prisoner. Romeo ran off to Friar Lawrence's house.

Someone had already gone to tell the Prince of 25 Verona about the killing of Mercutio and Tybalt. The Prince had said there must be no fighting in the streets, and he was soon on his way to see what had happened. He took with him Lord Montague, Lord Capulet and their wives. 30

When he arrived he ordered Benvolio to tell him why there had been a fight. Benvolio explained. He said that Romeo had not meant to fight Tybalt. But because

Tybalt had killed Mercutio, Romeo had become angry and had taken Tybalt's life.

Lady Capulet, who did not know that Romeo was now her daughter's husband, wanted Romeo put to
5   death for what he had done. Lord Montague said that Romeo had done the right thing in killing Tybalt, a murderer. The Prince, who wanted no trouble, ordered Romeo to leave the city. Romeo would never be allowed back. He could not live in Verona any more.

10   The Prince could not let Romeo break the law. If anyone was killed on the streets of Verona, the murderer must be punished.

Chapter Two

Juliet was still waiting for her Romeo to come to take her away. Instead, her nurse brought her the terrible news that Romeo had killed her cousin, Tybalt.

At first Juliet was angry at what he had done, for she 5 did not know how hard he had tried to stop the fight. But, when she heard that Romeo had been sent away from Verona, her love for him became stronger than her anger. She was glad that Tybalt, who would have killed Romeo, had been killed first. Yet she was very sad that 10 she and her husband could not be together.

Juliet's nurse, who had brought the sad news, now tried to stop her crying. She said that she knew where Romeo was hiding. She said she thought that he would come and say goodbye to his new young wife before 15 he left.

Romeo is very sad

When Romeo reached Friar Lawrence's house, he told the priest everything that had happened. He was very sad. He thought Juliet would hate him because he had 20 killed her cousin. He thought he would be put to death.

Then he found out that the Prince had not ordered him to be killed. The Prince had said he must leave the city, instead. Romeo was not happy at all. He thought he would never see Juliet again. Living away from 25 Verona seemed just as bad as death.

At last, the nurse came with a message from Juliet, asking Romeo to come and see her. This made him a little happier. Now he knew that Juliet still loved him. He would be able to say goodbye to her before he went 30 away.

Friar Lawrence's advice

Friar Lawrence tried to make him cheerful. He hoped that there might be a happy end to all this trouble. Both Romeo and Juliet were alive and well, and perhaps the
5   Prince might forgive Romeo, later. He thought that their marriage might still bring to an end the quarrel between the two families.

The priest advised Romeo to stay for a while in the city of Mantua, which was not far away. He would be
10   able to hear all the news about Verona. He must wait there for the right time to return and ask the Prince to forgive him. Romeo listened to his advice, and got ready to go and see Juliet before he left the country.

This second meeting at night was both joyful and sad.
15   The rest of the family were in bed. Romeo and Juliet were happy to be together again, even if it was only for a few hours. At the same time, they were sad because they had to part, perhaps for ever. As the sun began to rise, Romeo said it was time for him to go. The other
20   Capulets in the house were now waking up. If they discovered him, they would take his life.

Romeo promised to write to Juliet from Mantua. He told her that they might one day be able to live happily together. He kissed her goodbye, and quietly went
25   away.

Juliet must marry Count Paris!

In the early morning, Juliet's mother, Lady Capulet, came into her daughter's room. She found Juliet looking quite ill. Her face was pale, and wet with tears. She
30   thought that Juliet had been crying because of the death of her cousin, Tybalt.

Lady Capulet had brought some news that she hoped would make Juliet forget what had happened. She hoped this news would be a happy surprise for her daughter.

Old Lord Capulet, not knowing about Juliet's marriage to Romeo, had chosen a husband for her. The man's name was Count Paris, and he was rich and good-looking. Lord and Lady Capulet thought that Juliet would be pleased and proud to have Paris as her husband. There was no good reason to wait, and the wedding would be in a few days' time.

This was the news which Lady Capulet told Juliet. Instead of making Juliet happy, it just made her even more sad.

Juliet's parents are angry

Juliet thought of many excuses to try to stop the marriage. She said she did not know Paris well enough to marry him; that she was still too young to get married; it was too soon after the death of her cousin, Tybalt. She could not tell her parents the real reason, which was that she was married already.

Her parents were angry. Her father thought she was being difficult for no good reason. Speaking very cruelly, he ordered her to be ready to marry Paris on the next Thursday.

Juliet turned to her mother, hoping that she would help her, but Lady Capulet would not listen. Even her old nurse, whom Juliet had told about her marriage to Romeo, was against her. She said that since Juliet could not have Romeo, it was foolish of her to refuse to marry Paris!

Poor Juliet! At last she decided to go to talk to Friar Lawrence. She told her parents she was going to talk to him about the wedding.

The priest already knew of the coming marriage.

Count Paris had visited him to arrange things for it, and he was still there when Juliet arrived. Paris left, as it would not be right for him to stay while Juliet was with the priest.

5   'I shall come for you,' he said to her, 'early on Thursday morning.'

Alone with the priest, Juliet asked for his help and advice. She would do anything he said, but she could not give up Romeo and marry Paris. She would even kill
10   herself if that was necessary.

Friar Lawrence's dangerous plan

The good priest loved both Romeo and Juliet. He told her how he thought they might be able to stop the wedding. His
15   plan was a dangerous one. Juliet would need to be very brave.

'Go home,' he said, 'and be happy. Say you will marry Paris. Tomorrow is Wednesday; sleep alone tomorrow
20   night. Don't let your nurse stay in the room with you. Take this bottle, and when you are in bed, drink what is in it.' Friar Lawrence put a small bottle into her hand.

25   He said that when Juliet had drunk what was inside it, she would seem to be dead for the next two days. When Paris came to get her in the morning, he would think she was dead. She would then
30   be taken to the family tomb, where the bodies of all the dead Capulets were placed.

If she was brave enough to do all this, she would wake, as if from a deep sleep, in forty-two hours. 'I shall

send a letter to Romeo,' said the priest. 'I shall ask him
to come to the tomb to meet you when you wake up.
Then he will take you away with him to Mantua.'

Juliet was pleased with the plan. She went home,
ready to do as Friar Lawrence had told her. She found   5
her parents busy arranging the marriage party. As she
now seemed ready to obey her father's wishes, he was
very pleased that she had been to see the priest.

'I am sorry,' said Juliet. 'I will marry Paris, if that is
what you want.' She pretended to be interested in   10
choosing her wedding dress and the jewellery she
would wear.

Paris had come to see the tomb of the girl who should have been his wife. He did not know about Romeo's love for Juliet. He only knew that the Capulets and

5 Montagues hated each other. He thought that Romeo had come to do something terrible to the dead bodies of his enemies. So he angrily asked Romeo to

10 stop.

Romeo told Paris he would kill him if he did not go away. They started to fight, and Paris was killed.

15 As he died, he cried, 'If you are a kind man, open this tomb and lay me with Juliet.'

Romeo picked up his lamp to see who it was that he had

20 killed. He saw Paris who, he had heard, was going to marry Juliet.

He felt sorry

25 for him, so he lifted the body and laid it at the side of Juliet in the tomb. Then he took a last look at his Juliet, kissed her, quietly drank the poison, and died.

Friar Lawrence comes to the tomb

The messenger whom Friar Lawrence had sent to Mantua,

30 had not arrived. There had been an accident on the way. When the priest heard about it he hurried to the tomb,

so that he would be there when Juliet woke up. He did not think that Romeo would be there.

Friar Lawrence came alone, carrying an iron bar. As he walked in the dark towards the church, Romeo's servant came towards him. He had stayed away from the tomb, as Romeo had ordered him not to go near. This man told the priest to hurry. He knew something was wrong.

The priest felt very much afraid. What was that light he could see burning just outside the tomb? What was this blood on the ground? Whose bodies were these inside the tomb? He came near and saw Romeo and Paris lying dead at Juliet's side.

'Where is my Romeo?'

Juliet was just beginning to wake from her long sleep. She opened her eyes and saw the priest standing in front of her. Slowly, she began to remember where she was. 'Where is my Romeo?' she asked the priest.

Friar Lawrence was just going to reply, when he heard a sound. People were coming to the tomb. The servant of Paris had run away when he saw his master fighting with Romeo, and was now bringing some men back with him.

The priest was afraid of being found with the dead bodies. He asked Juliet to come away quickly and hide. But Juliet had seen Romeo by her side. She would not move. So the priest left her, and went and hid a little way off.

Juliet saw that Romeo was dead. She saw the cup still in his hand. She at once knew that he must have drunk poison because he had thought that she was dead. Taking Romeo's knife, Juliet pushed it into her own heart, and killed herself.

Friar Lawrence explains

The men saw that there had been a fight. Then they saw the three dead bodies. They would not let the servants of Paris and Romeo go away. They also held the priest, who had been found hiding near by. They sent for the Prince of Verona and the parents of Romeo, Juliet and Paris.

There, outside the tomb, Friar Lawrence sadly told everyone the whole story. Here are his words:

'Romeo there, dead, was Juliet's husband and she there, dead, was Romeo's wife.' He pointed to them as he spoke. 'I married them. Their wedding day was the day on which Tybalt was killed and Romeo was sent away.

'Juliet was unhappy because Romeo had to leave her, not because of the death of her cousin, Tybalt. And you,' the priest pointed to Lord Capulet, 'told her she must marry Count Paris.

'She came to me and asked me to find some way to stop this second marriage. I gave her a sleeping medicine to take so that she would look dead. I wrote to Romeo, asking him to be here tonight to help me to take Juliet away. But my messenger was stopped by an accident, and last evening my letter was returned to me.

'So I came alone to take Juliet from the tomb, when she woke. I was going to keep her with me in secret until I could send for Romeo. When I got here, I found Paris and Romeo dead. Then Juliet woke up. She asked for Romeo. I was going to tell her what had happened, when I heard someone coming. I asked her to go outside and hide, but she had seen Romeo and would not leave him. Then she must have killed herself.'

The servant of Paris told them how the fight had started, and Romeo's servant described how his master had ridden that night from Mantua.

So the whole sad story became clear.

Then the Prince of Verona turned to Lord Montague 5
and Lord Capulet. He told them that if they had ended their quarrel long ago, this terrible thing might not have happened. So, at last, the two sad old men turned to one another and promised that they would be friends, and at peace, for the rest of their lives.   10

As You Like It

Chapter One

In the land of France, there lived a Prince called Prince Senior. He did not live in a beautiful palace, and he had no lands of his own. Everything had been taken from him by his wicked younger brother, Prince Frederick.

5   Prince Senior now lived in the Forest of Arden. This was a large and beautiful wood, far away from his old home. Some of his good friends and servants had gone there with him. They did not want to stay with the wicked younger brother in his palace. They were much
10   happier living in the forest with Prince Senior.

    Prince Senior had a beautiful daughter, called Rosalind, but she did not live in the Forest of Arden with her father. She had wanted to go with him, but Prince Frederick made her stay at his palace. He did this
15   because of his own daughter, Celia.

    Celia and Rosalind were very good friends. Prince Frederick knew that if Rosalind went to live in the Forest of Arden, his own daughter would want to go and live there with her. So he made Rosalind stay with
20   him. Rosalind liked being with Celia, but she was often sad when she thought about her father. Celia did all she could to help her cousin to be happy.

Charles the wrestler

One day Rosalind and Celia were sitting in the palace
25   garden when a servant came by. The servant told them that there was going to be a wrestling match in the garden. The two girls wanted to know all about it.

He told them that a wrestling match was a fight between two men. Each man tried to hold the other and throw him down on to the ground. The man who was left standing was the winner.

A very famous wrestler was staying at Prince Frederick's palace. The man's name was Charles. The servant said that Charles was so strong and so clever he always won. Only a few days before he had thrown down three brothers, one after the other. The brothers were large, strong men, but Charles had nearly killed them all.

Celia and Rosalind felt quite frightened. They did not want to see anything as cruel as a wrestling match. But then Prince Frederick arrived. He said that the match would begin very soon, so they would have to stay and see it.

Prince Frederick also said that a very young man, who had come to fight Charles, would probably get hurt. He had asked the man not to fight, but the man said he wanted to. Prince Frederick felt sorry for the young man, and he asked Rosalind and Celia to speak to him. Perhaps they could make him decide not to fight.

Orlando will fight Charles

Rosalind and Celia talked to the young man. He was very good-looking. They tried to tell him not to fight.

'It does not matter if I die,' he said, 'I have no friends. I shall fight, and you must wish me luck!'

Rosalind and Celia said they hoped that he would win.

'I am not very strong,' said Rosalind, 'but I wish that my little strength could be added to yours.'

The young man left the two girls. He wanted to get ready for the wrestling match. The name of this good-looking young man was Orlando.

Oliver talks to Charles

5   Orlando lived with his older brother, Oliver. Their father, who had been a friend of Prince Senior, had died when Orlando was a small boy.

Oliver was a wicked man. He had always been very cruel to his young brother, Orlando. He did not send
10 him to school and he did not let him have lessons at home. However, Orlando had grown into a good, kind man, like his dead father. Oliver hated Orlando because everyone liked him.

When Orlando decided to fight with Charles the
15 wrestler, Oliver soon heard about it. Charles himself had gone to tell Oliver. He was afraid that if he hurt Orlando, Oliver would be angry with him.

Oliver was not angry. He was pleased at the thought. He believed his brother would be badly hurt if he
20 fought Charles. He decided to try to make Charles angry with his brother so that he would fight him harder.

He said to the wrestler, 'Orlando is not a good young man. He is always making trouble for me, his own
25 brother. He does not listen to me. I advised him not to fight with you, but he took no notice. He is too proud, he gets angry quickly, and he is very dangerous. If you only hurt him a little, he will come back to you later and kill you for it. There is no one I know who is more
30 wicked than he is. Break his neck, if you like. No one will be sorry or angry with you about it.'

When the wrestler heard this, he went away, promising that he would show no kindness to Orlando.

Oliver had then gone to Orlando. He pretended to wish him luck in the fight. He did everything he could to make Orlando angry with Charles the wrestler, so that he would put his life in danger.

Orlando had said to Oliver that it did not matter if 5 he lost, or was killed in the fight. He did not want to live because his life at home was so unhappy.

Rosalind and Orlando fall in love

When Rosalind saw Orlando, she didn't want him to be killed. Then, as the fight began, she prayed that he 10 would win.

Perhaps her prayers helped Orlando. Charles was very strong, but his strength was not enough to hold on to Orlando. After a while everyone saw that Orlando was a better wrestler than Charles. Then Orlando threw 15 Charles heavily, and the big wrestler lay on the ground. He could not move or speak; his strength was all gone. Orlando was the winner.

Prince Frederick asked Orlando who he was. When Orlando told him his father's name, the Prince was not pleased. He remembered that Orlando's father had been a close friend of his brother, Prince Senior.

'I wish you had been the son of any other man,' he said, and left the garden. He was angry that the son of his old enemy had been successful in the fight.

Rosalind was very happy when she heard that Orlando's father had been a friend of her own father. She had fallen in love with the brave young man. After the competition she went to speak to him. She took a gold chain from around her neck, and gave it to him.

'Wear this for me,' she said, 'I would give you more if I could.'

Orlando, who had received very little kindness in his life, was pleased. He thought Rosalind was very lovely, and fell in love with her. He liked her so much that he could only look at her. He could not speak. Rosalind and Celia went back into the palace before he could think of anything to say.

Rosalind must leave the palace

Soon after this someone told Orlando that Prince Frederick was angry with him. It would not be safe for him to stay there. So he left the palace at once. Rosalind felt sad because Orlando had gone away. Celia tried to make her cheerful, but it was no use.

At this time Prince Frederick decided he did not like Rosalind any longer. She was good and kind, and the people felt sorry for her because of her father. Perhaps, also, he was angry with her for liking Orlando, whom he hated.

One day, while Celia and Rosalind were talking about Orlando, the Prince came into their room. He told Rosalind that she must leave the palace at once. 'If, in ten days time, you are found any nearer to this palace than twenty miles, you will die,' he said.

Poor Rosalind asked what she had done to make him so angry. 'You are your father's daughter; that is enough!' was the only answer he gave her.

Celia spoke to her father, and asked him to let

Rosalind stay, but it was no good. The Prince would say no more.

Celia decides to leave with Rosalind

Celia liked her cousin too much to let her go away alone. 'When my father told you to go away, that was the same as telling me to go away, too,' she said. 'We are such good friends. What happens to you must happen to me, also. I don't care what you say, I am coming with you.'

So they decided that they would go together. They would try to find Rosalind's father in the Forest of Arden.

The two girls were young, pretty, and rich, and they were both the daughters of princes. It would be dangerous for them to travel through the country in their rich-looking clothes.

'Let us put on plain and poor clothes so that people will think that we are country people,' said Celia. 'We can put some colour on our faces, too, to make them look dark. We will not be beautiful any more. People will think we have been out in the sun all day.'

'Yes,' said Rosalind, 'and it might be safer if one of us dressed like a man. I'll do that, because I am taller. I shall call myself "Ganymede".'

The two girls dressed themselves in their country clothes, took some money and some jewellery, and left the palace. No one saw them go.

Chapter Two

At the same time as Rosalind and Celia were planning to run away from Prince Frederick, Orlando was also planning to leave his cruel brother. After the wrestling competition, he had gone home. An old servant met him at the gate of the house. The man's name was Adam. He had always loved Orlando and served him well.

Orlando must leave his home

'My dear master,' said Adam, 'you must not stay here. Your brother, Oliver, has heard that you won the fight with Charles the wrestler. He is so angry that he plans to set fire to your room tonight. If you do not die, then I'm sure he will find another way of killing you. You must keep away from this house.'

'But Adam,' said Orlando, 'where can I go? I have no money. I cannot become a beggar, or go about robbing people to get food.'

Adam replied that he had enough money to give Orlando. He would go with him, for he did not want to stay with the wicked Oliver.

'O good old man!' cried Orlando. 'We will go together. And I hope that before all your money has been spent, we shall find some way of earning a living.'

So Adam and his master went away together. They walked towards the Forest of Arden, where the good Prince Senior, Rosalind's father, and his friends had their camp.

Rosalind and Celia in the Forest of Arden

Rosalind and Celia, dressed like country people, reached the edge of the Forest of Arden safely.

In this part of the country there were very few houses. The two girls were hungry, and they wanted to find somewhere to stay for the night, but they did not know where to go. All they could see around them were trees. 5

They walked and walked through the trees, until they were too tired and too hungry to walk any more. Rosalind wanted to cry, but she remembered that she was no longer Rosalind, a woman, but Ganymede, a man. It would not be right for a young man to sit down 10 and start crying.

Rosalind and Celia buy a farm

At last they met an old man. Rosalind asked him where they could buy food and where they could stay for the night. 15

'This young girl,' said Rosalind, trying to speak like a man, 'is so hungry and tired that she cannot walk any more. Please tell us where we can find food and shelter for the night. We have plenty of money to pay for it.'

The old man replied, 'I wish I could help you, but 20 there is little I can do. Everything I have belongs to my master – my land, my sheep, even my house. Now he wants to sell them all, so I can give you nothing.'

'If your master wants to sell the land, the sheep and the house, then we shall buy them,' said Rosalind. 25 'We will pay you some money, too, if you will stay and look after the sheep for us.'

So the old man, who was a shepherd, and whose name was Corin, gave them food and a place to sleep. They bought the house and stayed there. 30

Orlando comes to the Forest

Rosalind did not forget Orlando. She knew that she

loved him, and wanted to see him again. She did not know that he, too, had left home. She did not know that he, with his old servant, Adam, had gone in the same direction as she and Celia. She did not know that
5   they were also in the Forest of Arden.

When Orlando and Adam reached the forest, they, too, found that it was difficult to get food and shelter. For a long time they walked round and round under the trees.

The old man became ill because he was so hungry.
10   He had to sit down on the ground. He told Orlando to leave him where he was. He said he thought he was going to die.

Orlando carried him to the shelter of a big tree, and laid him down gently. 'Don't talk about dying, Adam,'
15   he said. 'Rest here while I go and get something for us to eat. I shall come back very soon.'

Orlando finds food

Now the good Prince Senior and his friends were living in a camp in the forest close to this place. Orlando
20   found them. They were sitting under some trees. In front of them was a lot of food and drink. They were just going to start eating a meal.

Orlando did not know that the people he could see were the Prince and his friends. They looked like very
25   rough people. He thought that they might be robbers.

He was not afraid, and he was hungry. He ran up to them. He pulled out his sword and cried, 'Eat no more, eat no more, give me food!'

The Prince was surprised, but when Orlando had
30   explained everything, he told the young man to go and bring old Adam. He promised that he and his friends would not eat anything until Orlando and Adam came back to the camp.

When Orlando returned with Adam, he saw that the Prince had kept his word. The food had not been touched. They were given as much food as they could eat.

Then the Prince spoke to Orlando. He discovered that Orlando was the son of his old friend, and he was very pleased. He told Orlando and Adam that they could stay at his camp for as long as they wanted.

Love poems for Rosalind

The house where Rosalind and Celia were living was also not far away from the Prince's camp. One day Rosalind, who was still dressed as the young man, Ganymede, had a strange surprise. She found a piece of paper fixed on to a tree. On the paper was a poem, about Rosalind. It said some nice things about her, but it was not a very well-written poem.

She was reading the poem to herself when she met Celia. Celia, too, had a piece of paper with a poem about Rosalind on it. Celia said she had seen the name 'Rosalind' cut into some of the trees in the forest.

Rosalind could not think who had done it. She thought it was very strange because she was still dressed as Ganymede. No one in the forest knew she was Rosalind. The writing must have been done by someone who had known her before she came to the forest.

She asked Celia who she thought it was and Celia told her it must be Orlando. She said she had seen Orlando lying under a tree. He was dressed like a hunter.

Rosalind meets Orlando, and then her father

As they were talking about it, they saw two men coming

towards them. The girls hid themselves and, as the men came nearer, Rosalind saw that one of them was Orlando. His friend was making fun of him for writing poems to Rosalind and fixing them on to the trees.

5 The young ladies came out of their hiding-place, and spoke to Orlando. He did not know them and he thought that Rosalind was a young man.

Orlando and Ganymede became good friends. Rosalind, as Ganymede, talked with Orlando about his
10 love for Rosalind.

Orlando said he was very ill because he was so much in love. She said she could help him so that he would not feel ill any more, but he must tell her all about this person, 'Rosalind'. Of course, she wanted to make him
15 talk about how much he loved her.

The days passed happily. Rosalind even forgot that she was looking for her father, the Prince. Then one day he met her in the forest. He noticed that the young man, Ganymede, looked very much like his daughter,
20 Rosalind.

He stopped her and asked her what her name was, and who her parents were. She replied that her name was Ganymede and that her parents were as good as he was. The Prince was very amused. He never thought
25 that what she said was true.

Chapter Three

Soon after this a strange thing happened to Orlando.
He was walking alone in the forest when he saw
someone lying asleep under a tree. He was surprised
when he saw who the stranger was. It was Oliver, his   *5*
cruel brother. He was dressed in torn, old clothes.
His face was dirty and he looked most unhappy.

Orlando fights a lion

As he looked closer, Orlando saw that a snake was lying
around his brother's neck. When it saw Orlando, the   *10*
snake slid away into the forest. Orlando watched it go.
Then he saw a lion hiding behind a small tree, waiting
to jump out at the sleeping man.

   At first, Orlando thought that he would let the animal
kill Oliver. Why should he help Oliver who had always   *15*
been so cruel to him? But Orlando was too kind to let
his brother die, and too brave to run
away from the lion.

He ran forward quickly and attacked it with his sword.
He killed it. But when he was fighting it, it hurt his arm.

Oliver and Orlando are friends

The noise of the fight woke Oliver. He could not
5 believe what he saw. There stood the brother whom he
hated, but who had just saved his life.

Oliver had come to the forest to kill his brother. He
had been sent to look for him by Prince Frederick. After
the wrestling match, the Prince had decided to have
10 Orlando killed. But Orlando had gone away before he
could be taken prisoner.

Prince Frederick had ordered Oliver to bring Orlando
back, dead or alive. If he could not do so by the end of
a year, he would lose all his money and lands. So
15 Oliver had gone to look for his brother, but had got
lost in the forest, and had gone to sleep. Then Orlando
had come along and saved him from the snake and the
lion.

Oliver felt very sorry for the things he had done to
20 Orlando in the past. He asked Orlando to forgive him.
Orlando did forgive him, and from that day Oliver loved
Orlando as a brother should.

Rosalind faints

At midday on the day when Orlando saved his brother's
25 life, he had promised to meet his friend, Ganymede.
But, because of his fight with the lion, he could not
keep his promise. So, to show why he could not come,
he asked Oliver to take a handkerchief to Ganymede.
The handkerchief was covered with blood from his arm.
30 Rosalind, still dressed as a man, was waiting for
Orlando when Oliver came. He explained who he was,

and what had happened to Orlando. He gave her the handkerchief.

When she heard that it was her lover's blood on the handkerchief Rosalind fainted. Her face went white, she felt very weak, and she fell to the ground. Then she remembered, just in time, that she was Ganymede, a man. She tried to explain that she had only pretended to faint. However, Oliver and Celia had to help her walk home. Then she sent Oliver back to Orlando.

But now Rosalind and Orlando were not the only people in love. For when Oliver saw Celia he fell in love with her, and she with him. So Oliver had a lot to tell Orlando when he returned.

'When I showed Ganymede your handkerchief,' he said, 'your young friend almost fainted.'

Then Oliver told Orlando that he had fallen in love with Celia. He said he had decided to marry Celia and live with her in the forest for the rest of his life. 'As for our father's lands,' he added, 'I give them all to you.'

Orlando was very happy for his brother. 'Let your wedding be tomorrow,' he said. 'I will ask Prince Senior and his friends to come.'

Wedding plans

Oliver went to find Celia to tell her the good news. Rosalind, dressed as Ganymede, came to see Orlando.

Ever since she had heard that her lover had been hurt by a lion, Rosalind had wanted to come and see him. She was pleased to see that he was not badly hurt. Orlando told her that Celia and Oliver were getting married the next day.

'I am very glad,' said Orlando, 'that my brother will marry the girl he loves. But oh, if only I could marry my dear Rosalind!'

When Rosalind heard him say this, she thought that she must soon change back to herself once more.

'If you wish to marry Rosalind tomorrow,' she said, 'tomorrow Rosalind shall come here, and you shall have your wish. Believe me, I can make your Rosalind come. Since I was three years old, I have often talked to a wizard, a strange old man who taught me how to make magic. With his help, I shall be able to do as I have promised.'

Orlando almost believed what she said.

'Put on your best clothes. Ask all your friends to come,' Rosalind continued. 'If your wish is to marry Rosalind tomorrow, then tomorrow you shall marry her.'

Rosalind is herself again

On the next day, therefore, they all met. Ganymede went with Orlando to the Prince.

'If I bring your daughter, Rosalind, to you,' Ganymede said to the Prince, 'will you let her marry Orlando?'

'I will,' the Prince replied.

'And do you say that you will marry Rosalind, Orlando, if I bring her here?'

'I will marry her,' said Orlando.

Ganymede and Celia then left. Everyone thought they were just going to get ready for the wedding. Ganymede took off his man's clothes, put on a woman's dress, and became the Lady Rosalind. Celia changed her poor country dress for one of her own, and appeared as the Lady Celia once more.

Then they went back to the Prince and Orlando. Everyone was very surprised.

Rosalind went straight to her father and kissed him. Orlando, looking at her, saw that she was Rosalind, whom he had wanted so much to see again. The Prince told Rosalind that he was very happy that she was going to marry Orlando. He greeted Celia, his niece, and Oliver. So they were all married in the forest. After that there was a great wedding feast, with plenty of good food to eat, and wine to drink. 5

Prince Senior gets his lands back

While they were all still eating and drinking, a messenger arrived, with news for the Prince. 'Prince Frederick,' he said, 'has given you back your country.' 10

He told them all how Prince Frederick had got an army and had started out to attack his brother in the Forest of Arden. As he had entered the forest, he had met a priest. This man had talked with him for a long time and, at last, Frederick saw how wicked he had 15 been. He decided to give up everything, and to spend the rest of his life as a priest. So he sent a message to his brother, promising to give him back his country. He also promised the Prince's friends that they could have back their money and lands. 20

So the story ended happily for the Prince and the lovers.

QUESTIONS AND ACTIVITIES

CHAPTER 1

Put the notes about these people in the right boxes.

1 **Puck** (a) Egeus wants him to marry Hermia.	2 **Hermia** (b) Queen of the elves and fairies.	3 **Lysander** (c) An elf; the servant of King Oberon.
4 **Helena** (d) She will not obey her father.	5 **Demetrius** (e) Hermia wants to marry him.	6 **Titania** (f) Hermia's best friend.

CHAPTER 2

Put the reasons in the right boxes.

This happened ...	because ...
1 Puck put juice on Lysander's eyes 2 Helena woke Lysander up 3 Helena was angry with Lysander 4 Hermia went to look for Lysander 5 Everyone ran away from Bottom 6 Queen Titania woke up	(a) his head had become a donkey's head, (b) she thought an animal had killed him. (c) she thought he might be dead. (d) she heard Bottom singing. (e) he thought Lysander was Demetrius. (f) she thought he was making fun of her.

CHAPTER 3

*Put the names in the right gaps. You will have to use some names more than once. Choose from: **Helena, Hermia, Puck, Oberon, Demetrius, Lysander.***

Oberon put some juice into Demetrius's eyes, but he had forgotten that (1) ____ was now in love with Helena. Demetrius woke up. He saw (2) ____, and fell in love with her. Now, both men said they loved (3) ____. Neither of them loved (4) ____. Later, (5) ____ told (6) ____ to put the juice of a different flower in (7) ____ 's eyes. When they woke, (8) ____ was his old self, and loved (9) ____ again. (10) ____ still loved Helena.

CHAPTER 4

Choose the right words to say what this part of the story is about.

Viola and Sebastian were on their way to **Italy/Illyria** when their ship broke (2) **up/down** in a storm. Viola was saved. She wanted to work for Orsino, the (3) **Prince/King** of Illyria. She dressed up as a (4) **girl/boy**, and called herself (5) **Sebastian/Cesario**. Viola fell in love with Orsino, but he loved Olivia. He asked his (6) **servant/friend** Cesario (really (7) **Sebastian/Viola**) to take a letter to Olivia. Then Olivia began to fall in love with (8) **the Prince/Viola**.

CHAPTER 5

Put the underlined sentences into the correct paragraphs.

1   Sir Toby Belch was Olivia's uncle. <u>This made Olivia angry.</u> He often sang noisily and behaved badly.
2   Sir Toby thought, Sir Andrew Aguecheek would be a good husband for Olivia. <u>Malvolio had scolded him for drinking too much.</u> She did not like Sir Andrew.
3   Sir Toby was angry with Olivia's servant, Malvolio. <u>He was a fat, noisy man who often drank too much wine.</u> Sir Toby wanted to make Malvolio look stupid.

CHAPTER 6

Use these words to fill the gaps: **prisoner, captain, friend, officers, purse, garden.**

Antonio was the (1) ____ of the ship that had brought Sebastian to Illyria. He saw Viola fighting Sir Andrew Aguecheek in Olivia's (2) ____. He thought Viola was his (3) ____, Sebastian, and went to help. When the (4) ____ made him a (5) ____, he was angry because his friend would not give him his (6) ____.

CHAPTER 7

Put the letters of these words in the right order. The first word is 'daughter'.

Romeo met Lord Capulet's (1) **tregahud**, Juliet, and fell in love with her. Sadly, the Capulets were (2) **inmeese** of Romeo's (3) **mayfil**, the Montagues, but Friar Lawrence thought the (4) **agmirare** might help the two families to become friends. Then Juliet's (5) **unsoci**, Tybalt, killed Mercutio, and Romeo killed Tybalt. When the (6) **recnip** was told he said that Romeo must leave Verona.

CHAPTER 8

Choose the right words to say what happens.

Juliet did not want to marry (1) **Tybealt/Paris**, so Friar Lawrence gave her some (2) **medicine/wine** to drink when she was alone in her room on Wednesday (3) **night/morning.** Juliet would seem to be (4) **ill/dead** for two days. The Friar would (5) **give/send** a letter to Romeo asking him to take Juliet with him to (6) **Mantua/Verona**.

CHAPTER 9

Put the names in the right gaps. Use some names more than once: **Romeo, Juliet, Paris, Friar Lawrence, Capulet.**

Romeo heard that Juliet had died. He did not receive the letter from (1) ____, so he did not know that (2) ____ was not really dead. At the (3) ____'s tomb, (4) ____ saw Romeo trying to break in. They fought, and (5) ____ killed (6) ____. Romeo saw (7) ____ lying in the tomb. He drank some poison, and died. When (8) ____ woke up she saw that he was dead. She was so sad that she took (9) ____'s knife, and killed herself with it.

CHAPTER 10

*Use these words to fill the gaps: **dangerous, wrestler, hurt, brother, kill, little.***

Charles was a famous (1) ____ who always won every fight. A young man called Orlando wanted to fight with him. Orlando's elder (2) ____, Oliver, wanted Charles to (3) ____ Orlando. He told Charles that Orlando was very (4) ____, and that if he only hurt him a (5) ____ in the fight, Orlando would come back later and (6) ____ him.

CHAPTER 11

Some of these statements are true, and others are false. Which are the true ones?

1 Rosalind found a poem about her fixed on to a tree.
2 Celia said she thought Ganymede must have written it.
3 When Orlando met Rosalind he did not know her.
4 Rosalind looked like an old man, and she said her name was Ganymede.
5 'Ganymede' asked Orlando to tell him all about Celia.
6 She wanted to hear him say how much he loved her.

CHAPTER 12

Put the words at the end of these sentences in the right order.

1	Oliver was asleep, and had a …	[around] [his] [lying] [neck] [snake].
2	A lion was waiting …	[out] [to] [jump] [him] [on].
3	Orlando killed the lion but …	[his] [it] [hurt] [arm].
4	When Oliver woke …	[had] [he] [saw] [happened] [what].
5	He was sorry for what …	[Orlando] [had][he] [to] [done].

English Readers

G

Al
V

The Call of the Wild and
   Other Stories
Jack London

Emma
Jane Austen

Jane Eyre
Charlotte Brontë

Little Women
Louisa M. Alcott

**The Lost Umbrella of Kim
   Chu**
Eleanor Estes

**Tales From the Arabian
   Nights**
Edited by David Foulds

Treasure Island
Robert Louis Stevenson

   Stories
O. Henry

Lord Jim
Joseph Conrad

**A Midsummer Night's Dream
   and Other Stories from
   Shakespeare's Plays**
Edited by David Foulds

Oliver Twist
Charles Dickens

**The Talking Tree and Other
   Stories**
David McRobbie

Through the Looking Glass
Lewis Carroll

**The Stone Junk and Other
   Stories**
D.H. Howe

GRADE 2

**The Adventures of Sherlock
   Holmes**
Sir Arthur Conan Doyle

A Christmas Carol
Charles Dickens

**The Dagger and Wings and
   Other Father Brown Stories**
G.K. Chesterton

**The Flying Heads and Other
   Strange Stories**
Edited by David Foulds

**The Golden Touch and
   Other Stories**
Edited by David Foulds

**Gulliver's Travels —
   A Voyage to Lilliput**
Jonathan Swift

GRADE 3

**The Adventures of Tom
   Sawyer**
Mark Twain

**Around the World in Eighty
   Days**
Jules Verne

**The Canterville Ghost and
   Other Stories**
Oscar Wilde

David Copperfield
Charles Dickens

Fog and Other Stories
Bill Lowe

**Further Adventures of
   Sherlock Holmes**
Sir Arthur Conan Doyle